LEARNING TOGETHER

ADVICE AND INSTRUCTIONS ON COMPLETING THESE TESTS

1. There are 85 questions in each test. Make sure you have not missed a page.

2. Start at question 1 and work your way to question 85.

3. If you are unable to complete a question leave it and go to the next one.

4. Do not think about the question you have just left as this wastes time.

5. If you change an answer make sure the change is clear.

6. Make sure you spell correctly.

7. You may do any rough work on the test paper or on another piece of paper.

8. Each test should take approximately 50 minutes.

9. When you have finished each test mark it with an adult.

10. An adult may be able to explain any questions you do not understand.

TEST 11

1. Write down any letter which occurs once in REVERBERANT and twice in RESONANCE.

(_____)

2. Write down any letter which occurs twice in CONDENSATION and twice in EVAPORATION.

(_____)

3. Which letter occurs in JOANNE but not in JOAN?

(_____)

4. A number plus one third of six equals 10. What is the number?

(_____)

Share 15 apples between Janet and John so that for every ONE apple Janet gets John gets TWO apples.

5. How many apples does John get?

(_____)

6. How many apples does Janet get?

(_____)

7. How many less than John did Janet get?

(_____)

In the questions below TWO words must change places so that the sentences make sense. Underline the TWO words that must change places.

Look at this example: The **wood** was made of **table**.

8. The fan had broken its car belt.

9. When they climbed to the rain the top had stopped.

10. The ship sailed anchor and lifted away.

11. A page was note from the torn book.

12. What dinner we having for our are to-day?

The table below gives some information about the addition of numbers in the left hand column to numbers in the top row. Complete the table.

	+	0.3	2.2	1.4
	0.7	1.0	2.9	2.1
13, 14,	1.6	1.9		
15, 16	1.2	1.5		

In the following questions write in the brackets one letter which will complete the word in front of the brackets AND the word after the brackets.

Look at this example: ROA (D) OOR.

17. BOTTO (____) OUSE.   18.   FU   (____) AT.

19. VER   (____) ACHT.   20.   CRIS   (____) RICE.

21. WRIN   (____) RAIN.   22.   BEN   (____) EAR.

Complete the sequences by inserting the correct numbers or letters in the brackets.

A B C D E F G H I J K L M N O P Q R S T U V W X Y Z

23.   **A**   **D**   **F**   **I**   (_____)

24.   **ZY**   **WV**   **SR**   **NM**   (_____)

25.   **FGH**   **EFG**   **DEF**   **CDE**   (_____)

26.   **WV**   **TU**   **SR**   **PQ**   (_____)

27.   **1.5**   **3.0**   **4.5**   **6.0**   (_____)

28.   **25**   **21**   **17**   **13**   (_____)

29   **162**   **54**   **18**   **6**   (_____)

30.   **9.8**   **10.9**   **12**   **13.1**   (_____)

In each line below a word from the left-hand group joins with one from the right-hand group to make a new word. The left-hand word always comes first. <u>Underline the chosen words.</u>

Look at this example:

CORN	<u>FARM</u>	TIME	OVER	FIELD	<u>YARD</u>
31. FOR	LONG	DAM	TELL	CAST	SAKE
32. BLISS	DEEP	DAM	TEAR	PEN	SELL
33. ROBE	JERK	TALK	ART	IN	LIKE
34. PASS	FEW	SAD	ABLE	ILL	DOCK
35. TAB	OVER	INN	LET	TUNE	LOW
36. TALE	ON	MAN	TILL	OR	TELL

In the sentences below there are 4 words missing. Choose the MOST SUITABLE words from the lists A to D to complete the sentences. Choose a word from list A for space A, a word from list B for space B and so on.

Underline the words you choose.

As the weather got more (A) we (B) together to try to keep (C). We hoped that soon the people would begin to (D) for us.

37A.	38B.	39C.	40D.
pleasant	cried	dry	pray
wet	walked	warm	hope
miserable	shivered	hungry	talk
deteriorate	laughed	awake	search
hot	huddled	asleep	cry

£43.97 was made up using the smallest number of notes and coins shown below. How many of each were used?

41. £10 notes   (____)   42. 50p coins   (____)   43.   20p coins   (____)

44. 2p coins   (____)   45. 1p coins   (____)

Thermometers are drawn below. The arrows point to temperatures. Read the temperatures and enter them into the brackets below the thermometers.

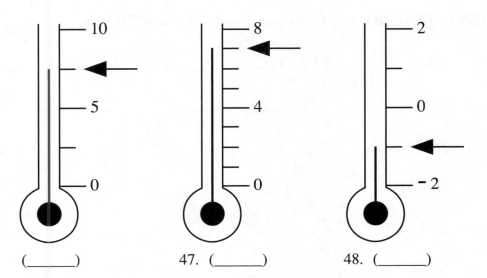

46.   (____)   47. (____)   48. (____)

Arrange the following words in alphabetical order.

enclose,   emery,   emend,   enamel,   emerge.

49.(_____) 50.(_____) 51.(_____) 52.(_____) 53.(_____)

First   **last**

Oldborough School has three lessons each afternoon. Each lesson, except the second lesson, lasts for the same length of time. There is a 5 minute gap between each lesson. Complete the table below, which shows the times at which lessons begin and end.

		Begins	**Ends**
54.	First Lesson	1.25 pm	
55.	Second Lesson		2.35 pm
56.	Third Lesson		3.15 pm

In the following questions a letter can be taken from the first word and put into the second word to form TWO new words. Write both NEW words.

Look at this example: THEN   TANK   (TEN)   (THANK)

The H moves from THEN to TANK and makes the new words TEN and THANK.

57. LATHER   TICK   (_____)   (_____)

58. FIORD   BAT   (_____)   (_____)

59. RINSE   KIT   (_____)   (_____)

60. LANCE   HARM   (_____)   (_____)

61. THERM   GALLEY   (_____)   (_____)

62. MAIZE   NOSE   (_____)   (_____)

63. FIRST   COW   (_____)   (_____)

64. CAMPS   ARROW   (_____)   (_____)

In each question below a man <u>ALWAYS STARTS</u> by facing <u>NORTH</u>.

Decide which directions he would be facing if he made the following turns -

65. He turned a quarter turn clockwise followed by a three-quarter turn
anti-clockwise.   (_____)

66. He made a three-quarter turn clockwise, followed by a half turn anti-clockwise
and then a quarter turn clockwise.   (_____)

67. He turned through 360 degrees.   (_____)

A word of FOUR letters is hidden in each of the sentences below. The hidden words begin at the end of a word and finish at the start of the next word.

Write the hidden words in the brackets.

Look at this example:
Ti<u>me</u> <u>an</u>d tide wait for no man. The answer is MEAN.

68. She attached the bow to the parcel.   (_____)

69. I hope they are allowed to go.   (_____)

70. The large kangaroo munched the green grass.   (_____)

71. This is something you must do especially as it is so important.   (_____)

72. The climber found a hidden cave in the mountains.   (_____)

73. The landscape altered as we drove across the country.   (_____)

Five children A, B, C, D and E returned from holiday with sticks of rock, games and toys as presents. Only B and D didn't have sticks of rock.
B was the only person with just one present and it was a game.
Only A and E did not have games. 4 children had toys.

74. Who brought only games and toys home?   (_____)

75. Who brought 3 presents home?   (_____)

76. Which 2 children had the same presents?   (_____)

77. Altogether how many presents were taken home?   (_____)

In the following questions one word can be put in front of each of the given words to form a new word.

Write the correct words in the brackets.

Look at this example: shell   shore side   bird   (SEA)

78. get   land   night   summer   (_____)

79. dog   fire   powder   boat   (_____)

80. cast   pour   stream   trodden   (_____)

81. look   coat   throw   haul   (_____)

In each of the following questions the numbers in the second column are formed from the numbers in the first column by using the same rule. Put the correct answer in the bracket for each question.

82. 6 ⟶ 12   83. 36 ⟶ 5   84. 5 ⟶ 12

     7 ⟶ 14   25 ⟶ 4   6 ⟶ 14

     8 ⟶ 16   81 ⟶ 8   10 ⟶ 22

     9 ⟶ (____)   49 ⟶ (____)   17 ⟶ (____)

85. 18 ⟶ 8

    14 ⟶ 6

    12 ⟶ 5

     6 ⟶ (____)

TEST 12

1. Which letter, occurring more than once, occurs as often in GEOSYNCLINE as it does in GENTLEMEN?   (＿＿＿＿＿)

2. Which letter occurs once in HUNDREDWEIGHT, once in KILOGRAM but not in WEIGHING?   (＿＿＿＿＿)

3. Which letter occurs as often in LAWLESS as it does in LAW-MAKER but does not occur in JUDGE?   (＿＿＿＿＿)

4. Charles adds 9 to a third of a number and gets 27. What is half of that number?   (＿＿＿＿＿)

5. Chocolate bars cost 7p. more than lollipops. Two bars and one lollipop cost 53p. How much for one lollipop?   (＿＿＿＿＿)

In the questions below TWO words must change places so that the sentence makes sense. Underline the TWO words that must change places.

Look at this example: The _wood_ was made of _table_.

6. The television turned the child on.

7. The man took the picture framed to be valued.

8. The sun soon dried and blistered in the paint.

9. A computer program pressed the wrong button and lost the operator.

10. His present told him to choose a mother and put it in the car.

The table below gives some information about the addition of numbers in the left hand column to those in the top row.
Complete the table correctly using only the numbers given.

28.75,   22.7,   5.1,   35.95,   2.5,   27.3

+		9.7	
17.6			20.1
26.25	31.35		

11. 12.

13. 14.

15. 16.

TEST 12 PAGE 1

In each line below write in the brackets one letter which completes the word in front of and the word after the brackets.

Look at this example: ROA (D) OOR

Here D completes ROAD and begins DOOR.

17. FOREIG   (____)   EWT

18. CRA   (____)   NU

19. ELUD   (____)   LBOW

20. GEA   (____)   EIGN

21. SOCIA   (____)   IBEL

In each line below, the first word can be changed into the last word in three stages.
Only ONE letter can be replaced at a time and proper words must be made each time.

Look at this example: tide   (ride) (rode)   rope

22. hail   (_____)   (_____)   pull

23. pink   (_____)   (_____)   cane

24. fact   (_____)   (_____)   lake

25. kerb   (_____)   (_____)   head

26. chin   (_____)   (_____)   shop

In each line below underline TWO words, ONE from each side, which together make ONE correctly spelt word. The word on the left always comes first.

Look at this example:

<u>BLACK</u> ALL TOP   AND **<u>BIRD</u>** BOY

27.	DO	NOT	IS		NOW	SENT	ICE
28.	BAG	BOOK	KNOW		AGE	LED	CASE
29.	PAGE	GLOW	FAR		ANT	BEE	ASS
30.	PLOUGH	STIR	HERE		RING	UP	ON
31.	BUD	ADD	SUIT		ON	IN	OR
32.	VICAR	WEST	STUN		AGE	LAW	ANT

In each of the following questions the letters of a word have been jumbled up. Using the clue unjumble the letters and write the correct word in the brackets.

33.	EPNILCS	You can write with these.	(_____)
34.	RACAULLTCO	You can do sums on this.	(_____)
35.	DALINS	A piece of land surrounded by water.	(_____)
36.	DPCOKAD	A small field for horses.	(_____)
37.	ONPAWE	Object used for offence or defence.	(_____)

Write in the brackets a word that rhymes with the second word and has a similar meaning to the first word.

Look at this example: SICK MILL (____ILL____)

38.	ANSWER	STY	(_____)
39.	LIFT	HAZE	(_____)
40.	CROWD	ROB	(_____)

In the paragraph below five words are missing. Choose the most
appropriate words from the lists below. One word from list A fills the
space at A, one word from list B fills the space at B and so on.
Underline the words you choose.

The Hallowe'en fireworks (A) into the cold (B) night. The children (C) with
amazement as the rockets burst into a (D) of brilliant colours and lit up the (E) night
sky.

41. A	42. B	43. C	44. D	45. E
SLID	CHRISTMAS	GASPED	RIVER	BRIGHT
JUMPED	OCTOBER	SHOUTED	MIDDLE	WET
EXPLODED	FEBRUARY	HID	CASCADE	CLOUDY
FELL	EASTER	WHISPERED	STREAM	DAWN
HURRIED	JULY	SANG	PUDDLE	DARK

In the following questions a letter can be taken from the first word and put into the second word to
form TWO new words. The order of the letters is not changed. Write both NEW words.

Example:	THINS	TOUT	(THIN)	(STOUT)

46. TREAT   PINT   (_____)   (_____)

47. FIND   RUM   (_____)   (_____)

48. VOICE   WING   (_____)   (_____)

49. GNASH   LINE   (_____)   (_____)

50. BLACK   RUE   (_____)   (_____)

Complete the sequences by inserting the correct numbers in the brackets.

51. 23.37,   23.45,   23.53,   00.01   (_____)

52. 4.15,   3.25,   2.35,   1.45   (_____)

53. (34,43),   (41,35),   (48,27),   (55,19)   (_____,_____)

54. 2,   7,   14,   23,   34   (_____)

55. 1024,   256,   64,   16   (_____)

Using the numbers 8, 5, 6 and 4 ONCE ONLY in each question, fill in the spaces in any way that will make the statements correct.

Look at this example: (8 + 5 + 6 + 4)= 23

56. (____ X ____) - (____ X ____)   = 28

57. (____ + ____ + ____) X ____   = 76

58. (____ - ____) - (____ - ____)   = 1

59. (____ + ____) X (____ + ____)   = 130

60. (____ X ____) - (____ + ____)   = 11

In questions 61-66 the three words A, B and C are in alphabetical order.
The word at B is missing and you are given a dictionary definition instead.
Write the correct word in the space.

Look at this example: A) Flap
                             B) (__Flare__) Distress signal from a boat
                             C) Flash

61. A) ANVIL
     B) (_ _ _ _ _ _ _)   Uneasy with fear.
     C) ANY

62. A) PLACK
     B) (_ _ _ _ _ _)   A deadly epidemic.
     C) PLAICE

63. A) FOUND
     B) (_ _ _ _ _ _ _ _)   A jet of water.
     C) FOUR

64. A) HIPPODROME
     B) (_ _ _ _)   To engage for wages.
     C) HIRSEL

65. A) JABBER
     B) (_ _ _ _ _ _)   A wild, dog-like animal.
     C) JACKAROO

66. A) MOUSSE
     B (_ _ _ _ _)   Opening in the head of an animal.
     C) MOVE

In each question 67 - 70 the numbers in the second column are formed from the numbers in the first column by using a certain rule. A different rule is used in each question.
Put the correct answer opposite the arrow.

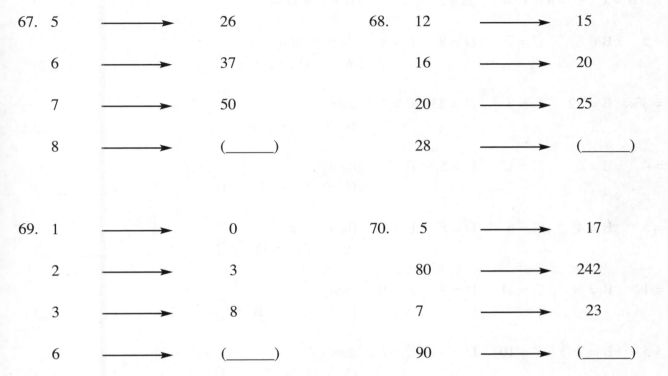

67. 5 ⟶ 26   68. 12 ⟶ 15

6 ⟶ 37   16 ⟶ 20

7 ⟶ 50   20 ⟶ 25

8 ⟶ (_____)   28 ⟶ (_____)

69. 1 ⟶ 0   70. 5 ⟶ 17

2 ⟶ 3   80 ⟶ 242

3 ⟶ 8   7 ⟶ 23

6 ⟶ (_____)   90 ⟶ (_____)

From the following shapes select the shape or shapes which satisfy the statements given. They may satisfy the statement on all or on some occasions. Answer the questions by placing the letter of the shape or shapes in the brackets.

A
PARALLELOGRAM

B
RECTANGLE

C
SQUARE

D
TRIANGLE

E
TRAPEZIUM

71. Diagonals are of equal length.   (_____)

72. Diagonals are at right angles.   (_____)

73. Three different sized sides.   (_____)

74. Internal angles total 180 degrees.   (_____)

In the following questions letters stand for numbers. Calculate the answer to each sum and write its LETTER in the bracket.

Look at this example:

A = 7   B = 2   C = 4   D = 1   E = 5   B + C + D =   (**A**   )

75. If A = 5   B = 6   C = 7   D = 8   E = 9   then
$$A + D - B \quad = \quad (_____)$$

76. If A = 33   B = 22   C = 3   D = 23   E = 2   then
$$B \times C \div E \quad = \quad (_____)$$

77. If A = 4   B = 6   C = 15   D = 5   E = 3   then
$$C \div E \times A - D \quad = \quad (_____)$$

78. If A = 5   B = 4   C = 6   D = 8   E = 3   then
$$A \times E - D - B \quad = \quad (_____)$$

79. If A = 12   B = 5   C = 11   D = 9   E = 10   then
$$E \times E \div B - D \quad = \quad (_____)$$

80. If A = 5   B = 2   C = 10   D = 4   E = 7   then
$$C \div A + E - D \quad = \quad (_____)$$

At one time £1 was worth 540 Greek drachma.
(In each question below the exchange rate is the same)

81. How many drachma was £3.00 worth?   (_____ drachma)

82. How many drachma was £6.25 worth?   (_____ drachma)

83. How many drachma was £13.75 worth?   (_____ drachma)

84. A man bought a souvenir for 2835 drachma.
How much was that in British money?   (£_____)

85. At the end of his holiday the man changed his money back into British money
and received £10.25. How many drachma did he have?   (_____ drachma)

TEST 13

1. Which letter occurs twice in INTERDICT, once in INTERCHANGE and three times in INTERDIGITAL?   (_____)

2. Which letter occurs as often in PIERCINGLY as it does in WHISTLES, but does not occur in PIGEON?   (_____)

3. Which letter occurs twice as often in DOMINEERING as it does in DONATION?   (_____)

4. Three times a number plus 5 is 44. What is twice that number minus 7?   (_____)

5. Throughout the winter a horse eats ⅓ of its bales of hay and ignores 64 bales of hay. How many bales of hay did the horse eat?   (_____)

In the questions below TWO words must change places so that the sentence makes sense. Underline the TWO words that must change places.

Look at this example.   The <u>wood</u> was made of <u>table</u>.

6. The grate burned brightly in the fire.

7. The untidy papers were covered with rooms.

8. The flowers been withered because they had not had watered.

9. The puncture by the tyre was caused in a nail.

10. The postman arrived with of sackful a mail.

The table below gives some information about the addition of numbers in the left-hand column to those in the top row.   Complete the table.

+		5.02
6.28	7.36	
	3.96	7.9
		5.1

11.
12.
13.
14. 15.

In each line below write in the brackets one letter which completes the word in front of and the word after the brackets.

Look at this example.　　　　ROA (D) OOR

16.　ARTIS　(_____)　ITLE

17.　SING　(_____)　LEGANT

18.　STAM　(_____)　RISON

19.　STEA　(_____)　AUGH

20.　GROI　(_____)　OURISH

In the following questions a letter can be taken from the first word and put into the second word to form TWO new words. Write both NEW words.

Look at this example:　　　THEN　　　TANK　　　(TEN)　　　(THANK)
The H moves from THEN to TANK and makes the new words TEN and THANK.

21.　BRAKE　　BASS　　　(_____)　　(_____)

22.　GRANGE　　RUB　　　(_____)　　(_____)

23.　LIED　　MOST　　　(_____)　　(_____)

24.　POUND　　HOSING　　　(_____)　　(_____)

25.　CLONE　　PANE　　　(_____)　　(_____)

In each line below underline TWO words, ONE from each side, which together make ONE correctly spelt word. The word on the left always comes first.

Look at this example:

<u>BLACK</u>	ALL	TOP	AND	**<u>BIRD</u>**	BOY
26. BLACK	WATER	ICE	VELVET	DOWN	FALL
27. BUT	SO	TAR	LID	ICE	NATION
28. DOOR	SEE	NOT	LAMB	WAY	LAMP
29. ON	CELL	SEED	SIZE	LING	OUT
30. LIE	HAND	EAR	MAN	WIG	HAT

Test 13 Page 2

Write in the brackets a word that rhymes with the second word and has a similar meaning to the first word.

Look at this example.   SICK MILL (___ILL___)

31. PIECE   IT   (_____)

32. TUG   SCHOOL   (_____)

33. WORK   SOIL   (_____)

In the sentences below five words are missing. Choose the most appropriate words from the lists below. One word from list A fills the space at A, one word from list B fills the space at B and so on.

Underline the word you choose.

The school children played happily in the (A) as the teacher sat at his desk. It was the last day of (B) and today the children would be breaking up for their Christmas Holidays. The (C) of Christmas made all the children very (D). They hoped that soon Santa would come and deliver all his (E).

34. A	35. B	36. C	37. D	38. E
CORRIDOR	DECEMBER	FEAR	LONELY	REINDEER
DOORWAY	WEEK	THOUGHT	GOOD	GIFTS
CLASSROOM	ALL	PAIN	TIRED	SNOW
GARAGE	HOLIDAYS	NOISE	EXCITED	DWARFS
HALL	TERM	SADNESS	ANXIOUS	CAKE

Two words inside the brackets have similar meanings to the words outside the brackets. Underline the TWO words each time.

Look at this example: horse, pig, cat   (falcon, <u>mouse</u>, snake, trout, <u>badger</u>)

39. walk   step   march   (parade fall paddle stride fly)

40. reservoir   cistern   panel   (tank sump water collect rain)

41. cod   mackeral   haddock   (shark pike herring whiting whale)

42. oak   chestnut   sycamore   (pine elm beech larch fir)

In the diagrams below each of the small rectangles are the same size.
What fraction of each diagram is shaded?

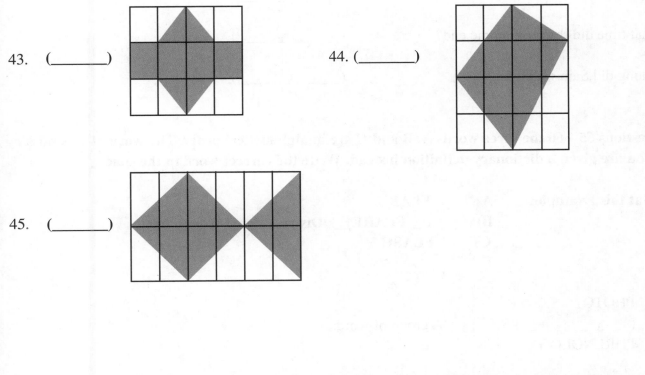

43. (_____)

44. (_____)

45. (_____)

In a certain code some words are written as follows. (The alphabet is printed to help you.)

A B C D E F G H I J K L M N O P Q R S T U V W X Y Z

SMILED	is written as	WQMPIH
TOWEL	is written as	XSAIP
CHAIR	is written as	GLEMV

Write the following words in code.

46. BOOKLET   (_____)   47. MONOLITH (_____)

48. PANIC   (_____)

What are these coded words in English?

49. FEOIVC   (_____)   50. QEGLMRI (_____)

51. STIVIXXE   (_____)

A television programme began at 16.55 and lasted for 55 minutes. Sam missed the first 15 minutes but saw the rest of the programme.

52. At what time did Sam begin to watch?   (_____)

53. At what time did the programme end?   (_____)

54. How long did Sam watch for?   (_____)

In questions 55 - 60 the three words A, B and C are in alphabetical order. The word at B is missing and you are given a dictionary definition instead. Write the correct word in the space.

Look at this Example: A)   **FLAP**
                            B)   **(__ FLARE__) Distress signal from a boat.**
                            C)   **FLASH**

        A)   PHOTO
55.   B)   (_ _ _ _ _ _)   A group of words.
        C)   PHRENOLOGY

        A)   URAL
56.   B)   (_ _ _ _ _)   Belonging to a city.
        C)   URCHIN

        A)   TIGHT
57.   B)   (_ _ _ _)   Slab of baked clay for covering roofs.
        C)   TILL

        A)   PORPOISE
58.   B)   (_ _ _ _ _ _ _ _)   Breakfast food, oatmeal boiled in water.
        C)   PORT

        A)   THAN
59.   B)   (_ _ _ _ _)   To express gratitude.
        C)   THAT

        A)   OUT
60.   B)   (_ _ _ _)   Egg shaped.
        C)   OVEN

Six towns A, B, C, D, E and F are at the points numbered 1-6 but not in that order. The arrow points to the North.

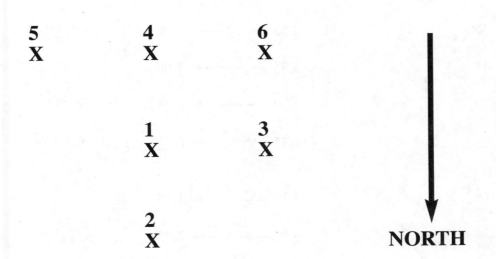

5
X

4
X

6
X

1
X

3
X

2
X

NORTH

Only one town is further North than towns A and C and this is not town D. Town B is due East of town F and due South of another town, which is not town C.

61. Which town is at point number 1?   (_____)

62. Which town is at point number 2?   (_____)

63. Which town is at point number 3?   (_____)

64. Which town is at point number 4?   (_____)

65. Which town is at point number 5?   (_____)

66. Which town is at point number 6?   (_____)

The words below and those in the lists are alike in some way. Write the letter of the list that each word belongs to in the brackets. Each letter may be used only once.

A	B	C	D	E
CASHEW	PLUTO	SPHERE	RICE	ALASKA
ALMOND	MINNIE	ORB	WHEAT	NEBRASKA
BRAZIL	MICKEY	BALL	BARLEY	HAWAII

67. GLOBE   (_____)

68. MILLET   (_____)

69. UTAH   (_____)

70. PEANUT   (_____)

71. DUMBO   (_____)

In each question 72 - 75 the numbers in the second column are formed from the numbers in the first column by using a certain rule. A different rule is used in each question. Put the correct answer opposite the arrow.

72. 9 ⟶ 35

11 ⟶ 41

7 ⟶ 29

4 ⟶ (_____)

73. 2.55 ⟶ 4.20

5.35 ⟶ 7.00

4.80 ⟶ 6.45

1.35 ⟶ (_____)

74. 3 ⟶ 18

5 ⟶ 34

7 ⟶ 58

9 ⟶ (_____)

75. 3.50 ⟶ 1.45

4.10 ⟶ 2.05

6.15 ⟶ 4.10

5.60 ⟶ (_____)

Using the numbers 2, 7, 5 and 6 once only in each question fill in the spaces in any way which makes the statements correct.

76. (_____ + _____ − _____) X _____ = 24

77. (_____ + _____) − (_____ + _____) = 4

78. (_____ + _____ + _____) ÷ _____ = 3

79. (_____ X _____) + (_____ X _____) = 47

80. (_____ X _____) + (_____ + _____) = 39

Complete these sequences, the alphabet is printed to help you.

A B C D E F G H I J K L M N O P Q R S T U V W X Y Z

81. C,   F,   H,   K,   M   (_____)

82. BZV   FXU,   JVT,   NTS,   (_____)

83. S,   T,   R,   U,   Q,   V   (_____)

84. T,   R,   N,   H,   (_____)

85. M,   O,   K,   Q,   I,   S   (_____)

TEST 14

1. Which letter appears the same number of times in the words DECISION and KESTREL? (_____)

2. Which letter occurs twice as often in NARCISSISM as it does in STOCKIST? (_____)

3. Which letter occurs less often in COMMISSION than in CLASSICAL? (_____)

4. In a garden there are three types of flowers. One third of them are roses. A quarter of the rest are carnations. There are 30 asters in the garden. How many carnations are there? (_____)

5. Tom has 45p. If John had 12p more he would have the same as Peter. If Tom spent one third of his money he would also have the same as Peter. How much does John have? (_____)

In the questions below TWO words must change places so that the sentences make sense. Underline the TWO words that must change places.

Look at this example: The <u>wood</u> was made of <u>table</u>.

6. The girl pavement a cat on the drew.

7. A pound pond fell into a coin.

8. Minor fog caused many dense accidents.

9. Without failed the radio batteries to work.

10. The clock was slow six minutes nearly this morning.

11. I help already done it without any have.

The table below gives some information about the addition of numbers in the left hand column to numbers in the top row.

Complete the table.

12	+	7.6		5.8
13. 14. 15.			9.7	
16. 17.	3.4		11.2	

In each question write in the brackets one letter which will complete both the word in front of the brackets and the word after the brackets.

Look at this example.   ROA (D) OOR.

18. ACOR   ( )   ASTY   19. EMI   ( )   URF

20. SING   ( )   ACH   21. PATI   ( )   ATH

22. SPIR   ( )   QUAL   23. VER   ( )   ULB

In each line below a word from the left-hand group joins one from the right-hand group to make a new word. The left-hand word comes first.
Underline the chosen words.

Look at this example: CORN <u>FARM</u> TIME OVER FIELD <u>YARD</u>

24.	GET	REST	OFF	FULL	LESS	HER
25.	OR	TRY	SIN	FARE	RING	DEAL
26.	FUR	MET	MORE	HOD	ALL	LEG
27.	CAB	SIT	TRIP	PET	LET	ILL
28.	MIST	OR	CAN	BUT	ERR	RUST
29.	ART	LET	SEA	PING	SON	HER

In the following questions a letter can be taken from the first word and put into the second word to form TWO new words. Write both NEW words.

Look at this Example: THEN TANK (TEN) (THANK)

The H moves from THEN to TANK and makes the new words TEN and THANK.

30.	PAINT	NOSE	(_____)	(_____)
31.	MORE	PAPER	(_____)	(_____)
32.	TAINT	NET	(_____)	(_____)
33.	FACTORY	FLING	(_____)	(_____)
34.	TABLE	GARAGE	(_____)	(_____)
35.	DINNER	DOOR	(_____)	(_____)

Five patients, a man, woman, boy, girl and baby are waiting to see a doctor. The girl is behind the baby but before the boy. The man is before the woman and she is one before the last. The girl is behind the man but he is not first.

36. First.   (_____)

37. Second.   (_____)

38. Third.   (_____)

39. Fourth.   (_____)

40. Fifth.   (_____)

In the sentences below there are 6 words missing. From the lists A to F choose the MOST SUITABLE words to complete the sentences. Choose a word from list A to fill space A, a word from list B to fill space B and so on. Underline the chosen word in each group.

The unicorn is an (A) animal that never lived. It was (B) to have the body of a horse with a single horn (C) the middle of its forehead. It was said that a unicorn could be (D) if someone stood in front of a tree and (E) aside as it charged. The horn would then become (F) in the tree.

41. A	42. B	43. C	44. D	45. E	46. F
FOOLISH	MEANT	AT	FOUND	WENT	SCRAPED
EXTINCT	ONLY	BESIDE	FRIGHTENED	WALKED	STUCK
IMAGINARY	INTENDED	OVER	CAUGHT	JUMPED	BENT
FUNNY	ALWAYS	IN	DISCOVERED	HOPPED	SHARPENED
SAVAGE	SUPPOSED	BEHIND	ANGERED	STOOD	SCORED

↑ **North**

* 47

* 48

* 49

* 50

* 51

* 52

The positions of 6 towns are shown. The towns are A, B, C, D, E and F.

Town F is further to the north than town E but is not the most northerly town.

B is directly south of one town and directly west of another.

Town A is south-east of C which is south-west of another town.

In the brackets enter the letter for each town.

47. (_____) 48. (_____) 49. (_____)

50. (_____) 51. (_____) 52. (_____)

| WAIT | HAM | LACK | VIEW | OFF | TRAY | BEE |
| MOAN | LIAR | MIGHT | TONGUE | ONE | | |

From the list above choose a word which rhymes with each of the following. Write the rhyming words in the brackets.

53. WHACK   (_____)   54. CHOIR   (_____)

55. FREIGHT   (_____)   56. COUGH   (_____)

57. PSALM   (_____)   58. QUEUE   (_____)

59. BONE   (_____)   60. QUAY   (_____)

Complete the following sequences. The alphabet is printed to help you.

A B C D E F G H I J K L M N O P Q R S T U V W X Y Z

61.	B	D	G	K	P	(_____)
62.	A	D	F	I	K	(_____)
63.	CZE	DYF	EXG	FWH		(_____)
64.	EXF	HUI	KRL	NOO		(_____)
65.	DWL	MEX	YNF	GZO		(_____)
66.	ZA	CU	QF	JN		(_____)
67.	AB	IJ	OP	ST		(_____)

In a code 2 3 4 6 1 and 1 2 3 4 5 represent two of the words

ROPES   PORTS   SPORT   POSER   SPORE.

Write each word in code.

68. ROPES   (_____)

69. PORTS   (_____)

70. SPORT   (_____)

71. POSER   (_____)

72. SPORE   (_____)

Decode the followiing.

73. 2 4 3 6 5 1 6   (_____)

74. 4 5 1 3 4 6   (_____)

75. 2 3 1 6 5 4 1   (_____)

The diagram below is made up of two triangles, a rhombus, a square, a rectangle and a parallelogram. By joining the points F I J, one of the triangles is made.

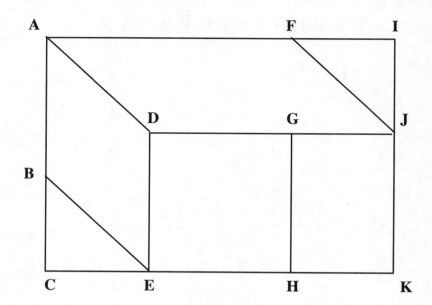

76. Which points join together to make up the other triangle?   (_____)

77. Which points join together to make up the square?   (_____)

78. Which points join together to make up the rhombus?   (_____)

79. Which points join together to make up the rectangle?   (_____)

80. Which points join together to make up the parallelogram?   (_____)

Using the numbers 3, 4, 5 and 6 ONCE ONLY in each question, fill in the spaces in any way that will make the statements correct.

Look at this example:

   3 + **4** + **5** + **6**   =   **18.**

81. (_____ + _____) − (_____ − _____)   =   6

82. (_____ + _____ + _____) X _____   =   45.

83. (_____ + _____) X (_____ − _____)   =   11.

84. (_____ X _____) − (_____ − _____)   =   11.

85. (_____ − _____) + (_____ X _____)   =   31.

TEST 15

1. Which letter occurs three times in ENCHANTING and twice in NATIONALITY? (_____)

2. Which letter appears twice in CONCENTRATES but not at all in RECESSION? (_____)

3. Which letter occurs as many times in UNYIELDING as it does in PRACTICE? (_____)

4. When three is subtracted from seven times a number the answer is 53. What is the number? (_____)

5. Twice 18 is the same as four times a number. What is the number? (_____)

A comic and two packets of crisps costs £1.05. A comic and one packet of crisps costs 75p.

6. How much is a comic? (_____)

7. How much is a packet of crisps? (_____)

In the questions below TWO words must change places so that the sentences make sense. Underline the TWO words that must change places.

Look at this example: The <u>wood</u> was made of <u>table</u>.

8. There for no key was the back door.

9. Have you spend money left to any?

10. Under the strain great cord broke.

11. Running not the corridor is in allowed.

12. Was supermarket checkout every very busy.

13. Under lay scattered books the table.

The table below gives some information about the subtraction of numbers in the left-hand column from numbers in the top row.

Complete the table

	−			
14. 15.		9.96		
16. 17.	2.73		4.12	
18. 19.		5.14		3.15

In each question write in the brackets one letter which will complete both the word in front of the brackets and the word after the brackets.

Look at this example:　　　ROA　(D)　OOR

20. MAL　( )　ORN　　　　　　21. CAS　( )　USH

22. TAME　( )　ORE　　　　　　23. LEA　( )　LOD

24. SOL　( )　IGHT　　　　　　25. SOD　( )　GAIN

In each line below a word from the left-hand group joins one from the right-hand group to make a new word. The left-hand word comes first. Underline the chosen words.

Look at this example: CORN　**FARM**　TIME　　　　OVER　FIELD　**YARD**

26.	JUST	SAT	TAKE		TAN	ICE	OR
27.	PAST	COMB	TOLD		AT	YOUR	MINE
28.	UP	OVER	DOWN		PAIR	SIT	HOLD
29.	SAD	CAT	AM		ILL	BUSH	ALE
30.	BUT	WAG	TO		ON	ERR	WERE
31.	USE	SAT	ACT		FULL	TING	OR

In the following questions a letter can be taken from the first word and put into the second word to form TWO new words. Write both NEW words.

Look at this example: THEN   TANK   (TEN)   (THANK)

The H moves from THEN to TANK and makes the new words TEN and THANK.

32. CANOE   SHUT   (_____)   (_____)

33. FLAKE   HALO   (_____)   (_____)

34. LEAD   SIZE   (_____)   (_____)

35. THREAT   SOW   (_____)   (_____)

36. CADGE   LAY   (_____)   (_____)

37. BALD   DARING   (_____)   (_____)

Roy is 6 years older than Harry who is 3 years younger than Ian.
Ian is 2 years older than Tom who is 4 years older than Sam.
Tom is 11 and Colin is 14.
List the boys in order from the youngest.

38. Youngest   (_____)

39.   (_____)

40.   (_____)

41.   (_____)

42.   (_____)

43. Oldest   (_____)

Groups of words are printed below. Each group is made up of words which are similar in some way.

A	B	C	D	E	F
daffodil	leopard	tango	penny farthing	kestrel	madam
daisy	puma	waltz	unicycle	hawk	tot
tulip	tiger	jive	bicycle	falcon	deed

Decide into which of the above groups the following words would fit.
Write the group letter in the brackets.
Use each letter once.

44. tandem (_____)   45. orchid (_____)

46. ewe   (_____)   47. merlin (_____)

48. ballet (_____)   49. panther(_____)

In a code, words are written as shown below.

APPLE   becomes   **DSSOH**   **WEATHER**   becomes   **ZHDWKHU**

Write the following words in code. The alphabet is printed to help you.

A B C D E F G H I J K L M N O P Q R S T U V W X Y Z

50. PORCUPINE   (_____)   51. WISDOM   (_____)

52. EXCEPT   (_____)

Decode the following words.

53. KBSKHQ   (_____)   54. FRQIOLFW (_____)

55. RUJDQLF   (_____)   56. UDGLVK   (_____)

V, W, X, Y and Z are five books.
V and X are story books and the others are non-fiction.
X and Y are not for children but the others are.
W and Y are not paperbacks but the rest are.

57. Which hardbacked book is a non-fiction adult book?   (_____)

58. Which paperback book is a children's story book?   (_____)

59. Which adult paperback is a story book?   (_____)

60. Is there a children's paperbacked non-fiction book?   (_____)

61. Is there an adult's hardbacked story book?   (_____)

In the following questions the numbers in the second column are formed from the numbers in the first column by using the same rule. Put the correct answer in the brackets for each question.

62. 1 $\longrightarrow$ 6   63. 11 $\longrightarrow$ 25   64. 2 $\longrightarrow$ 5

    3 $\longrightarrow$ 12   8 $\longrightarrow$ 19   6 $\longrightarrow$ 15

    6 $\longrightarrow$ 21   5 $\longrightarrow$ 13   8 $\longrightarrow$ 20

    9 $\longrightarrow$ (___)   0 $\longrightarrow$ (___)   11 $\longrightarrow$ (___)

65. 1 $\longrightarrow$ 5   66. 4 $\longrightarrow$ 1   67. 2 $\longrightarrow$ 3

    4 $\longrightarrow$ 20   10 $\longrightarrow$ 4   6 $\longrightarrow$ 9

    6 $\longrightarrow$ 40   16 $\longrightarrow$ 7   10 $\longrightarrow$ 15

    7 $\longrightarrow$ (___)   12 $\longrightarrow$ (___)   14 $\longrightarrow$ (___)

In each of the following questions 3 words are in alphabetical order. The second word has not been written but its meaning is given. Decide what the second word should be each time and write it in the brackets. Each dash in the brackets represents a letter.

Look at this example:

CROSS
(**CROWD**)   a large group of people.
CRUEL

NEWT
68. (_ _ _ _ _ _)   to take small bites.
NICKNAME

TEXTILE
69. (_ _ _ _ _)   upper part of leg.
TIDAL

FOAM
70. (_ _ _ _ _)   adjust to get a clear image.
FOUNDATION

SCREEN
71. (_ _ _ _ _ _ _ _)   write in a careless way.
SCRUB

MAMMAL
72. (_ _ _ _ _ _ _)   large dwelling house.
MARCH

WEASEL
73. (_ _ _ _ _)   mammal which lives in the sea.
WHEEL

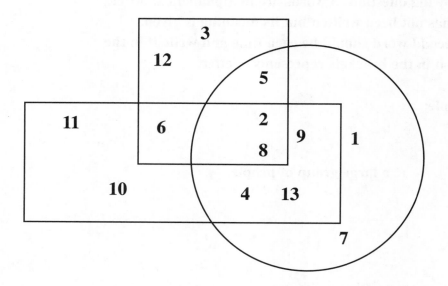

The following questions are about the numbers in the diagram above.

74. Which numbers appear in all three figures? (_____)

75. Which number is in both the circle and square but not in the rectangle? (_____)

76. Which numbers are in both the circle and rectangle but not in the square? (_____)

77. Find the sum of all the numbers which appear in one figure only. (_____)

78. Take the sum of the numbers that are in the square, but not the rectangle, from the sum of the numbers that are in the circle but not the square. (_____)

79. Take the sum of the numbers that are in the circle, but not the rectangle or square, from the sum of the numbers that are in the rectangle, but not the circle or square. (_____)

In the questions below give the next number in each series.

80.	37	21	13	9	7	(_____)
81.	1.9	3.7	5.5	7.3	9.1	(_____)
82.	1	8	27	64	125	(_____)
83.	3	8	18	38	78	(_____)
84.	2.75	4	5.25	6.5	7.75	(_____)
85.	(2,6)	(5,10)	(8,14)	(11,18)		(_____ , _____)

Answers to Test 11

#		#	
1.	N	44.	3
2.	A	45.	1
3.	E	46.	7.5 or 7 1/2
4.	8	47.	7
5.	10	48.	-1
6.	5	49.	EMEND
7.	5	50.	EMERGE
8.	FAN CAR	51.	EMERY
9.	RAIN TOP	52.	ENAMEL
10.	SAILED LIFTED	53.	ENCLOSE
11.	NOTE TORN	54.	2.00
12.	DINNER ARE	55.	2.05
13.	3.8	56.	2.40
14.	3	57.	LATER THICK
15.	3.4	58.	FORD BAIT
16.	2.6	59.	RISE KNIT
17.	M	60.	LANE CHARM
18.	R	61.	THEM GALLERY
19.	Y	62.	MAZE NOISE
20.	P	63.	FIST CROW
21.	G	64.	CAPS MARROW
22.	D or T	65.	SOUTH
23.	K	66.	SOUTH
24.	HG	67.	NORTH
25.	BCD	68.	HEAT
26.	ON	69.	REAL
27.	7.5	70.	ROOM
28.	9	71.	DOES
29.	2	72.	THEM
30.	14.2	73.	PEAL
31.	FOR SAKE	74.	D
32.	DAM PEN	75.	C
33.	JERK IN	76.	A and E
34.	PASS ABLE	77.	10
35.	TAB LET	78.	MID
36.	MAN OR	79.	GUN
37.	MISERABLE	80.	DOWN
38.	HUDDLED	81.	OVER
39.	WARM	82.	18 2X
40.	SEARCH	83.	6 Sq root X-1
41.	4	84.	36 2X + 2
42.	7	85.	2 Half of (X-2)
43.	2		

Answers to Test 12

#		#	
1.	N	44.	CASCADE
2.	R	45.	DARK
3.	W	46.	TEAT PRINT
4.	27	47.	FIN DRUM
5.	13p	48.	VICE OWING
6.	TELEVISION CHILD	49.	GASH LINEN
7.	PICTURE FRAMED	50.	BACK RULE
8.	SUN PAINT	51.	00.09 (24HR CLOCK)
9.	PROGRAM OPERATROR	52.	0.55 (-0.9)
10.	PRESENT MOTHER	53.	62,11 (+7,-8)
11.	5.1	54.	47(+5,7,9 ETC)
12.	2.5	55.	4 (÷by 4)
13.	22.7	56.	(8X6) - (5X4)*
14.	27.3	57.	(6+5+8) X 4*
15.	35.95	58.	(8-5)-(6-4)*
16.	28.75	59.	(8+5)X(6+4)*
17.	N	60.	(6X4)-(8+5)*
18.	G	61.	ANXIOUS
19.	E	62.	PLAGUE
20.	R	63.	FOUNTAIN
21.	L	64.	HIRE
22.	HALL HULL*	65.	JACKAL
23.	PINE PANE*	66.	MOUTH
24.	FACE LACE*	67.	65 (XSQ + 1)
25.	HERB HERD*	68.	35 (X + ¼x)
26.	CHIP SHIP*	69.	35 (XSQ - 1)
27.	NOT ICE	70.	272 (3X+2)
28.	BOOK CASE	71.	B,C,E**
29.	PAGE ANT	72.	B,C
30.	STIR RING	73.	D,E
31.	SUIT OR	74.	D
32.	VICAR AGE	75.	C
33.	PENCILS	76.	A
34.	CALCULATOR	77.	C
35.	ISLAND	78.	E
36.	PADDOCK	79.	C
37.	WEAPON	80.	A
38.	REPLY	81.	1620
39.	RAISE	82.	3375
40.	MOB	33.	7425
41.	EXPLODED	84.	£5.25
42.	OCTOBER	85.	5535
43.	GASPED		

*   There are other possibilities.
** Other combinations may work.

These are the answers to Book 3 of a set of 4 graded books. A child who has not previously attempted questions of this type may have difficulty with the first few tests. However, research shows that a child's ability to handle and understand these questions generally increases with practice.

website: www.learningtogether.co.uk   E-mail: info@learningtogether.co.uk   Learning Together, 23 Carlston Avenue Holywood Co Down BT18 ONF   Phone/Fax 028 90425852/028 90402086

Answers to Test 13

1. I
2. L
3. I
4. 19
5. 32
6. GRATE   FIRE
7. PAPERS   ROOMS
8. BEEN   HAD
9. BY   IN
10. OF   A
11. 1.08
12. 11.3
13. 2.88
14. 0.08
15. 1.16
16. T
17. E
18. P
19. L
20. N
21. BAKE   BRASS   RANGE
22. LED   GRUB
23. MOIST
24. POND   HOUSING
25. CONE   PANEL/PLANE
26. WATER   FALL
27. CAR   NATION/SO   LID
28. DOOR   WAY
29. SEED   LING
30. EAR   WIG
31. BIT
32. PULL
33. TOIL
34. CLASSROOM
35. TERM
36. THOUGHT
37. EXCITED
38. GIFTS
39. PARADE   STRIDE
40. TANK   SUMP
41. HERRING   WHITING
42. ELM   BEECH
43. 1/2
44. 1/2
45. 1/2
46. FSSOPIX
47. QSRSPMXL
48. TERMG
49. BAKERY
50. MACHINE
51. OPERETTA
52. 17.10
53. 17.50
54. 40 MINS
55. PHRASE
56. URBAN
57. TILE
58. PORRIDGE
59. THANK
60. OVAL
61. A
62. E
63. C
64. B
65. D
66. F
67. C
68. D
69. E
70. B
71. B
72. 20 (3X + 8)
73. 3.0 (+1.65)
74. 90 (XSQ. +9)
75. 3.55 (-2.05)
76. (2+7-5) X 6*
77. (7+5) - (2+6)*
78. (7+6+2) ÷ 5*
79. (7X5) + (2X6)*
80. (5X6) + (2+7)

Answers to Test 14

1. S
2. I
3. C
4. 10
5. 18
6. PAVEMENT   DREW
7. POND   COIN
8. MINOR   DENSE
9. FAILED   BATTERIES
10. SLOW   NEARLY
11. HELP   HAVE
12. 7.8
13. 1.9
14. 9.5
15. 7.7
16. 11.0
17. 9.2
18. N
19. T
20. E
21. O
22. E
23. B
24. REST   LESS
25. OR   DEAL
26. MET   HOD
27. TRIP   LET
28. MIST   RUST
29. SEA   SON
30. PANT   NOISE
31. ORE   PAMPER
32. TINT   NEAT
33. FACTOR   FLYING
34. TALE   GARBAGE
35. DINER   DONOR
36. BABY
37. MAN
38. GIRL
39. WOMAN
40. BOY
41. IMAGINARY
42. SUPPOSED
43. IN
44. CAUGHT
45. JUMPED
46. STUCK
47. D
48. C
49. F
50. B
51. A
52. E
53. E
54. LACK   LIAR
55. OFF   WAIT
56. HAM
57. VIEW
58. MOAN
59. BEE
60. BEE
61. V
62. N
63. GVI
64. QLR
65. PHA
66. LO
67. UV
68. 43251
69. 23461
70. 12346
71. 23154
72. 12345
73. PROTEST
74. RESORT
75. POSTERS
76. BCE*
77. DGHE*
78. ADEB*
79. GJKH*
80. AFJD
81. 5, 4, 6, 3**
82. 4, 5, 6, 3**
83. 6, 5, 4, 3**
84. 3, 4, 6, 5**
85. 4, 3, 6, 5**

Anwers to Test 15

1. N
2. T
3. E
4. 8
5. 9
6. 45p
7. 30p
8. FOR   WAS
9. SPEND   ANY
10. THE   GREAT
11. NOT   IN
12. WAS   EVERY
13. UNDER   BOOKS
14. 6.85
15. 7.97
16. 7.23
17. 5.24
18. 4.82
19. 2.03
20. H
21. P
22. E
23. P
24. E
25. A
26. JUST   ICE
27. COMB   AT
28. UP   HOLD
29. AM   BUSH
30. WAG   ON
31. ACT   OR
32. CANE   SHOUT
33. FAKE   HALLO
34. LAD   SEIZE
35. TREAT   SHOW
36. CAGE   LADY
37. BAD   DARLING
38. SAM
39. HARRY
40. TOM
41. IAN
42. COLIN
43. ROY
44. D
45. A
46. F
47. E
48. C
49. B
50. SRUFXSLQH
51. ZLVGRP
52. HAFHSW
53. HYPHEN
54. CONFLICT
55. ORGANIC
56. RADISH
57. Y
58. V
59. X
60. YES
61. NO
62. 30   3X + 3
63. 3   2X + 3
64. 27.5   ½X × 5
65. 53   XSQ + 4
66. 5   (X÷2) - 1
67. 21   1.5X
68. NIBBLE
69. THIGH
70. FOCUS
71. SCRIBBLE
72. MANSION
73. WHALE
74. 2, 8
75. 5
76. 4, 9, 13
77. 44
78. 14
79. 13
80. 6
81. 10.9
82. 216
83. 158
84. 9
85. 14, 22